MARVEL STUDIOS

THOR

C000131921

4 - **THOR** Fact File

6 - **Thor Comic Strip** Truth of History

14 - **LOKI** Fact File

16 - **Loki-like**

23 - **SIF** Fact File

26 - **ODIN** Fact File

34 - **THE WARRIORS THREE** Fact File

36 - **Asgardian Art**

38 - **HEIMDALL** Fact File

45 - **DESTROYER** Fact File

46 - **FROST GIANTS** Fact File

48 - **Warrior Vision**

58 - **Quest Test**

60 - **Which Asgardian Are You?**

BY ORDER OF *ODIN ALLFATHER*, KING OF ASGARD, AND PROTECTOR OF THE NINE REALMS, LET IT BE KNOWN THAT...

IS A MIGHTY WARRIOR WORTHY OF OWNING THIS SACRED TOME AND LEARNING THE SECRETS OF THE AESIR.

£7.99

THOR

To THE PEOPLE OF ASGARD, THOR IS REGARDED AS ONE OF THE REALM'S GREATEST WARRIORS. AS BRAVE AND COURAGEOUS AS THEY COME, THOR LIVES FOR THE THRILL OF BATTLE. NOTHING GIVES THIS FEARLESS WARRIOR GREATER PLEASURE THAN VANQUISHING THE ENEMIES OF ASGARD WITH HIS MIGHTY HAMMER, MJOLNIR.

MJOLNIR

Forged in the heart of a dying star from the Asgardian metal Uru, Thor's hammer is one of the most powerful weapons in all of the Nine Realms.

Mjolnir is virtually indestructible.

Once thrown, the hammer will always return to Thor's hand.

When wielding Mjolnir, Thor can command the lightning and the storm.

PRIDEFUL PRINCE!

Unfortunately, *Thor's* heroic reputation has made him arrogant and headstrong - something that worries his father *King Odin*. *Odin* knows that *Thor* must curb his reckless behaviour if he is to be a just and righteous leader when he inherits the throne.

COLD WAR!

His father's fears are proved right when *Thor's* rash actions bring *Asgard* to the brink of war with the *Frost Giants of Jotunheim*. Furious with his son, *Odin* strips *Thor* of his powers and banishes him to Earth.

BANISHED TO MIDGARD!

Forced to live in exile on *Earth* as a normal human, *Thor* must now face the realisation that he may never again return to *Asgard's* hallowed halls.

THOR
TRUTH OF HISTORY

In days gone by, the brave warriors of Asgard would often travel to Earth in search of adventure.

It was not unheard of for these warriors to interfere in the lives of humans, especially if they saw a great injustice that needed avenging. Throughout history, many blackhearted villains have found their plans to harm the innocent curtailed by the power of the Asgardians.

Over time, some of these incredible feats have become folk tales, whilst others have been lost to the sands of time. Read on to discover one of the untold tales of Asgard...

CONTINUED ON PAGE 17

LOKI

THE MASTER OF MISCHIEF

NATURAL CUNNING!

Unlike his older brother *Thor*, *Loki* is not a natural fighter. However, what he lacks in strength, he more than makes up for in cunning, preferring to use tricks and subterfuge, rather than brute force.

THE FORGOTTEN SON!

Unfortunately for *Loki*, the people of Asgard value strength and prowess in battle above all else. Consequently, he has always felt as if he lives in his brother's shadow and is jealous of the praise Thor receives, both from the Asgardian people and King Odin.

MAGIC OVER MIGHT!

But even though he's nowhere near as tough as his brother, *Loki* is no coward. Through years of studying ancient Asgardian texts he has taught himself to be a master of *magic and sorcery*. In battle, he can use these skills to devastating effect, disorientating his foes with incredible intricate illusions.

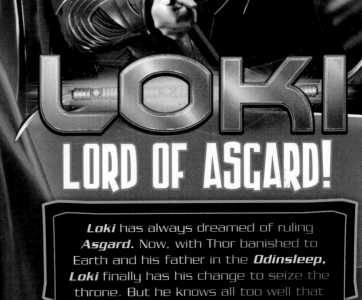

LOKI
LORD OF ASGARD!

Loki has always dreamed of ruling *Asgard.* Now, with Thor banished to Earth and his father in the *Odinsleep*, *Loki* finally has his change to seize the throne. But he knows all too well that his reign will only be temporary.

THE ETERNAL KING!

However, it seems that being the acting monarch isn't enough for Loki. In reality, he wants to rule Asgard forever and will stop at nothing to do so!

LOKI-LIKE!

EVEN MIGHTY HEIMDALL'S KEEN SENSES CANNOT SEE THROUGH MY SPELLS - A MERE HUMAN HAS NO CHANCE!

Loki's mastery of magic allows him to disorientate those around him with amazing illusions.

Can you see through his sorcerous tricks and spot which one of the apparitions below is the real Loki?

TURN TO PAGE 62 FOR THE ANSWER!

CONTINUED ON PAGE 37

SIF

Along with its ability to help Sif defend herself, her shield has sharp edges allowing it to be used as a weapon too.

WARRIOR MAIDEN!

Beautiful, bold and cunning, *Sif* is the greatest of all *Asgard's* warrior maidens. Though she is famed for her incredible fighting abilities, *Sif* does not care for stardom and prestige, and is only interested in the thrill and honour of battle.

FEARLESS FIGHTER!

In combat, Sif's skills with a sword and shield surpass any other and she has been known to fell monstrous creatures twice her size. She also has keen instincts and a sharp tactical mind that helps keep her one step ahead of her opponents at all times.

WARRIOR WORK-OUT!

HIDDEN HEROES!

A true warrior needs to have a keen mind, along with impressive skills in battle. So test your brains by seeing if you can spy where in this grid all these names are hidden!

[HOGUN]   [SIF]

[FANDRAL]   [ODIN]

[HEIMDALL]   [THOR]

[VOLSTAGG]

```
W F H V O S V C X K
Y P S L I N O D I N
H E I M D A L L C Q
C D F A Z U S K B O
K E R P T I T N E Y
G F A N D R A L B E
R N A R D S G M T A
F E F R A P G S H L
U T G A K R I Y O E
U H O G U N T L R S
```

ICE ROAD!

Here's a challenge that will chill the hearts of even the bravest adventurer! Can you find a way through the treacherous ice caverns of Jotunheim without running into any of the Frost Giants?

START

FINISH

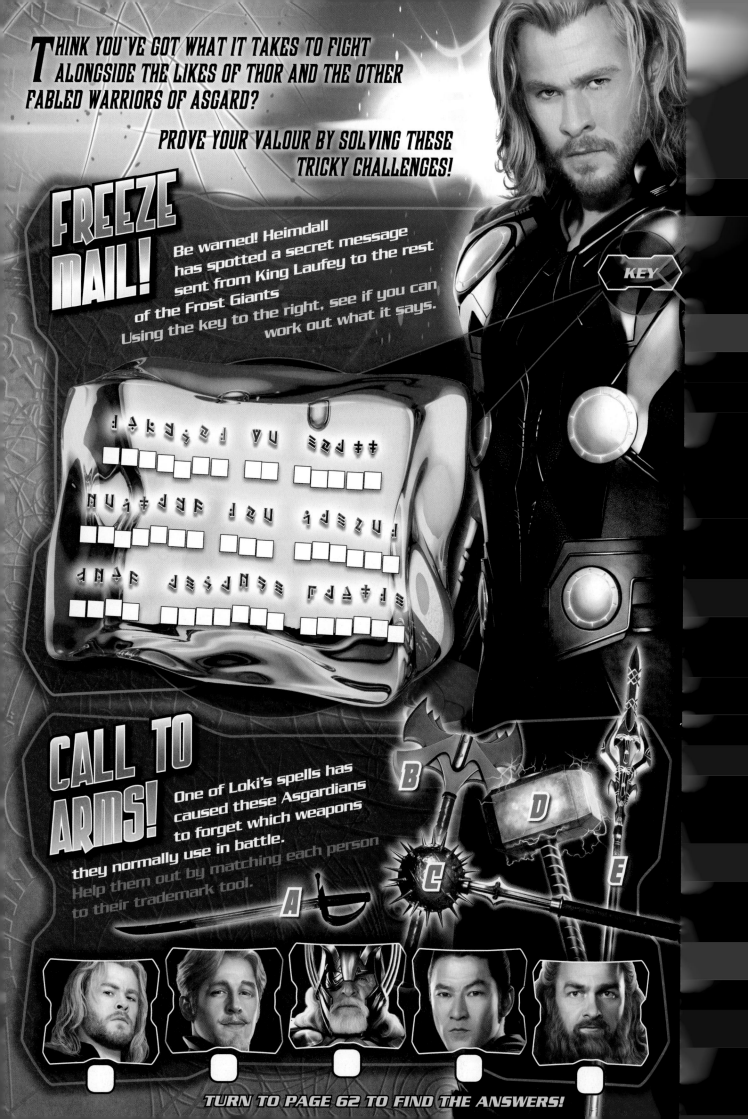

THINK YOU'VE GOT WHAT IT TAKES TO FIGHT ALONGSIDE THE LIKES OF THOR AND THE OTHER FABLED WARRIORS OF ASGARD?

PROVE YOUR VALOUR BY SOLVING THESE TRICKY CHALLENGES!

FREEZE MAIL!

Be warned! Heimdall has spotted a secret message sent from King Laufey to the rest of the Frost Giants. Using the key to the right, see if you can work out what it says.

KEY

CALL TO ARMS!

One of Loki's spells has caused these Asgardians to forget which weapons they normally use in battle. Help them out by matching each person to their trademark tool.

TURN TO PAGE 62 TO FIND THE ANSWERS!

ODIN
RULER OF ASGARD

REIGN OF THE ALLFATHER

A fair and wise King, *Odin* has ruled *Asgard* for thousands of years. Though during this time his kingdom has seen its fair share of war, he has now managed to broker a fragile peace between the people of the *Nine Realms*

THE ODINSLEEP

At certain times, *Odin* must enter a trance-like state known as the *Odinsleep*. Whilst in this frozen state, he cannot be woken until the *Odinforce* that flows through his body has been fully replenished. No one knows how long the *Odinsleep* will last each time, it could be a matter of days, months or even years.

HEIR TO THE THRONE

Before he next entered the *Odinsleep*, *Odin* planned to pass the rule of *Asgard* on to his son. But now *Thor* has been banished to *Earth*, it is uncertain who will become the new King.

GIZA

'TIS A PITY THOU CANNOT COMPREHEND MY WORDS, FAIR MAIDS, OR I WOULD SHARE WITH THEE SUCH TALES OF VALIANT ROVING AND FEARLESS ADVENTURING TO SET THY PRETTY LITTLE MINDS IN A WHIRL.

AND THERE IS MUCH TO TELL, THOUGH I BE NOT A BOASTFUL MAN...AS I AM SURE MY FRIENDS WILL ATTEST WHEN THEY ARRIVE--

THEY SHALL COME! OF THAT I AM CERTAIN...

...FOR THEY WILL BE LOST WITHOUT VOLSTAGG'S SAGE COUNSEL AND SUPPORT...

IT MAY TAKE SOME TIME FOR THEM TO ARRIVE, BUT ARRIVE THEY WILL...

...EVENTUALLY.

IN THE MEANTIME, I AM PLEASED TO ACCEPT ANOTHER FLAGON OF THAT DELICIOUS WINE, IF THOU PLEASE.

AH, SUCH WONDROUS HOSPITALITY.

IT DOES NOT SEEM CREDIBLE THE HELIOPOLITAN GODS WOULD AGREE TO LEAVE THIS PARADISE.

CONTINUED ON PAGE 40

33

THE WARRIORS THREE

Known for his high-spirits and charming nature, Fandral is an expert swordsman whose lightning fast skills with a rapier have earned him the nickname Fandral the Dashing.

The only thing Fandral loves more than the thrill of battle, is wooing maidens with tales of his past deeds. But despite his boastfulness, Fandral has a noble and courageous soul and will always do the right thing, even if that means putting himself in serious danger.

FANDRAL

Unlike his more jovial brother-in-arms, *Hogun the Grim* is a serious warrior who has no time for frivolity. Though a man of few words, what he does say is carefully considered and insightful, making him the voice of reason within the group. In battle, he is a methodical fighter, more concerned with getting the job at hand done, than defeating his foes with style and panache.

HOGUN, FANDRALL AND VOLSTAGG, BETTER KNOWN AS THE WARRIORS THREE, ARE THOR'S CLOSEST FRIENDS AND ALLIES. THEY ARE STAUNCHLY LOYAL TO THOR AND WILL HAPPILY FOLLOW HIM ON ANY QUEST – NO MATTER HOW DANGEROUS. THEIR PAST DEEDS ARE THE STUFF OF LEGEND AND MANY A SONG FILLS THE HALLS OF ASGARD TELLING OF THEIR HEROIC ADVENTURES.

HOGUN

VOLSTAGG

Volstagg the Voluminous is a larger than life warrior whose prowess on the battlefield is matched only by his appetite in the banquet hall. Though he may not be as graceful or nimble as his fellow warriors, he more than makes up for his lack of speed with his impressive strength. Few foes can stand up to a blow from his mighty two-handed axe.

COLOUR GUIDE

ART!

DO YOU THINK YOU CAN CREATE WORKS OF ART GOOD ENOUGH TO HANG IN THE HALLOWED HALLS OF ASGARD?

GRAB YOUR PENS AND PENCILS AND ADD A SPLASH OF COLOUR TO THESE IMPRESSIVE PORTRAITS!

COLOUR GUIDE

HEIMDALL

A MIGHTY WARRIOR EMPOWERED WITH AMAZING EYE-SIGHT, HEIMDALL IS ASGARD'S FIRST LINE OF DEFENSE AGAINST MONSTROUS INVADERS WHO SEEK TO DESTROY THE KINGDOM.

VISIONARY WARRIOR!

From his celestial observatory at the end of the *Rainbow Bridge*, he can see all that transpires throughout the *Nine Realms*. From the ice-fields of *Jotunheim* to the fiery, volcanic plains of *Muspelheim*, nothing escapes his mighty gaze.

THE BIFROST OBSERVATORY

The Asgardian machinery inside his observatory can use the *Bifrost* to open portals to other worlds. However, *Heimdall* is sworn to let no one pass through them unless they have permission of the King.

Along with being a mighty weapon, Heimdall's two-handed broadsword also acts as the key to activate the observatory's control panel.

'TIS DARK AND COLD HERE... AND MINE APPETITE IS SPOILED BY THE ODOROUS INCENSE...

...*SNIFF*... AND THE STENCH THE INCENSE SEEKS TO HIDE... MOST FOUL. LIKE ROTTING--

GIRL... WHENCE ARE WE BOUND?

I WAS CONTENT ABOVE IN THE LIGHT, SURROUNDED BY FOOD.

WHAT GOES ON... WHAT IS THIS PLACE?

THESE STERN ANCIENTS HAVE THE DEMEANOR OF PRIESTS, AND THEIR ACOLYTES LOOK NONE TOO FRIENDLY.

BONES! THIS IS SOME VILE CHARNEL PIT...

THOU MEAN TO SACRIFICE VOLSTAGG?!

MONSTERS. UNHAND ME. I AM A LORD OF ASGARD.

NO, YOU CANNOT DO THIS!

NOOO!

CONTINUED ON PAGE 49

DESTROYER

The Destroyer's Asgardian alloy skin is almost impenetrable and only the very best Asgardian weapons are powerful enough to pierce it.

SILENT SENTINEL

The Destroyer is an ancient *Guardian* who protects the dangerous weapons hidden within the *Royal Palace* vaults. Normally frozen like a statue, he will spring to life at a moment's notice, ready to strike anyone foolish enough to trespass in *Asgard's* hallowed treasure chambers.

LOYAL ALLY

Created by *King Odin,* the *Destroyer* will only obey the instructions of the current ruler of *Asgard.* No other creature in the *Nine Realms* can command this immovable and virtually *unstoppable warrior.*

The Destroyer can fire hugely powerful blasts of Odinforce energy that will disintegrate anything in their path.

THE FROST GIANTS

THE FROZEN WORLD OF JOTUNHEIM IS HOME TO A RACE OF BEINGS KNOWN AS THE FROST GIANTS. THESE POWERFUL BLUE-SKINNED CREATURES ARE A PROUD PEOPLE, WHO HAVE NO TIME FOR THOSE WHO INTRUDE UPON THEIR REALM.

WAR OF KINGS!

The Frost Giants are led by the ancient and imperial King Laufey. Though Asgard and Jotunheim have clashed many times in the past, Odin and King Laufey have now agreed upon a truce. But this peace is fragile at best and it would only take a small act of aggression by either side to plunge the two worlds into war once again.

FROZEN FIGHTERS!

Frost Giants have complete control over ice and can create dangerous ice spikes and spires to impale their foes.

Due to their super-cold bodies, anything a Frost Giant touches will be instantly frozen!

THE CASKET OF ANCIENT WINTERS

Created by the Frost Giants millennia ago, the Casket of Ancient Winters powered their cities and kept their planet alive. It is powerful enough to turn an entire realm into a land of snow and ice that only a Frost Giant could live in. Odin took the casket from the Frost Giants to protect other realms from their aggression and without the power of the casket, Jotunheim has slowly fallen into ruin.

ULTIMATE WEAPON!

It is currently hidden deep within Asgard's Weapons Vault. Even if the Frost Giants could get past the mighty Einher-jar Warriors who guard the vaults, they would still have to deal with the Destroyer. But they are willing to try, as retrieving the casket would give them the power to assault Asgard!

WARRIOR VISION!

See if your eyes are as good as Heimdall's, by spotting which Asgardians he has spied from his observatory.

A **B** **C** **D** **E** **F** **G**

1) SIF   2) HOGUN

3) VOLSTAGG   4) FANDRAL

5) ODIN   6) LOKI   7) THOR

QUEST TEST!

How closely were you paying attention to Thor and his friends' incredible quest? Take a look at these questions and see if you can answer them without looking back through the story. *Good luck!*

01. Which of the Warriors Three fell into Queen Nedra's mystical portal?

A) Fandral
B) Hogun
C) Volstagg

02. Which country did they end up in?

A) China
B) Egypt
C) Sweden

03. Take a look at this scene and see if you can remember what Thor said.

A) THOSE WHO WOULD ENSLAVE ANOTHER KNOW ONLY ONE LANGUAGE ... BRUTE FORCE!

B) THOSE WHO WOULD ENSLAVE ANOTHER KNOW ONLY ONE LANGUAGE ... MARTIAN!

C) THOSE WHO WOULD ENSLAVE ANOTHER KNOW ONLY ONE LANGUAGE ... THE LANGUAGE OF VIOLENCE!

Q4. What did Thor do with this banquet table?

A) Eat it all

B) Give it to the starving slaves

C) Have a food fight

Q5. Take a look at this picture from the story and see if you can spot the **four** changes.

Q6. What type of monster was hidden beneath the pyramid?

A) A Dragon

B) A Griffin

C) A Hippopotamus

Q7. Can you work out who has been removed from this picture?

A) Loki

B) Odin

C) Fandral

TURN TO PAGE 62 TO FIND OUT THE ANSWERS!

*T*HINK YOU'RE HEROIC ENOUGH TO STAND SHOULDER TO SHOULDER WITH ASGARD'S MIGHTIEST WARRIORS? TAKE THIS QUIZ TO FIND OUT!

START

KING LAUFEY HAS LAUNCHED A SURPRISE ATTACK AGAINST ASGARD.

DO YOU..?

Attack straight away!

Attack them!

UH OH, HE'S GOT A LEGION OF FROST GIANTS WITH HIM.

Do you jump into the fight straight away, or try to think up a new plan of attack?

Think of a new plan

OKAY, IF YOU SNEAK THROUGH THE PALACE'S CELLARS YOU'LL BE ABLE TO POP UP BEHIND LAUFEY AND BYPASS ALL HIS BODYGUARDS.

You could either head to the cellars or wait for your fellow warriors to turn up?

Fight!

IT'S FIGHTING TIME!

Fight Laufey!

Attack through the Cellars!

Wait fo back-up t attack

But which foe will you attack first? Battle Laufey, or have some fun dealing with his Frost giants?

Smash the Frost Giants!

[THOR]

Whilst you were scrapping, Laufey tried to steal the Casket of Ancient Winters. Luckily, the Destroyer stopped him but it was a close call. Like Thor, you're a brave and courageous warrior, but you need to learn to think before you act.

[SIF]

You managed to keep Laufey busy until your other fellow warriors arrived, but it was a really tough fight. Just like Sif, you're a clever warrior with the courage of an Asgardian!

Wait for your fellow warriors

Attack Laufey!

YOUR FELLOW WARRIORS WILL BE HERE IN A FEW MINUTES.

You could use the time to try to stop Laufey's plans yourself or let the others deal with him when they arrive?

IT SEEMS LAUFEY IS HEADING TO THE VAULT TO STEAL THE CASKET OF ANCIENT WINTERS.

Do you jump into the fight straight away, or try to think up a new plan of attack?

Leave it to the Destroyer!

THE DESTROYER HAS VANQUISHED THE FROST GIANTS AND ONLY LAUFEY AND HIS BODYGUARDS ARE LEFT.

Wait for the others

Try to capture Laufey!

You could find a way to capture Laufey or let him escape?

Let him escape

[HOGUN]

Laufey was so distracted by the other warriors, he had no chance defending himself from your surprise attack. You're as brave as they come with a keen tactical mind – just like Hogun.

[ODIN]

Laufey has learnt the hard way that attacking Asgard is a big mistake. It'll be a long, long time before he feels brave enough to try again. Like Odin, you're a fine warrior whose prowess in battle is matched only by your compassion.

[LOKI]

What a sneak! Without your help, the other warriors got pasted and Laufey stole the Casket of Ancient Winters. Like Loki, it seems you're only interested in looking after number one. I wouldn't be surprised if you were the one who told him to attack in the first place!

ANSWERS

LOKI LIKE!
PAGE 16

C

WARRIOR VISION!

PAGE 16

1 - SIF
2 - HOGUN
3 - VOLSTAGG
4 - FANDRALL
5 - ODIN
6 - LOKI
7 - THOR

WARRIOR WORK-OUT!
PAGE 24 - 25

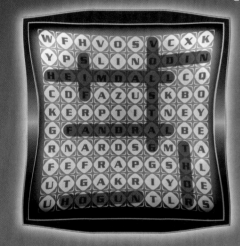

MESSAGE READS - TONIGHT WE SHALL RECLAIM THE CASKET FROM ASGARD'S VAULTS!

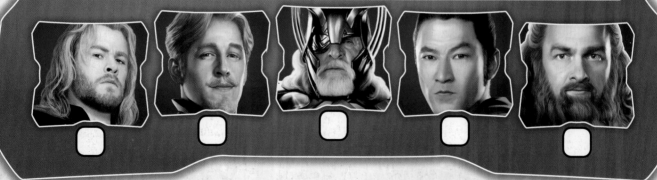

QUEST TEST!
PAGE 58 - 59

1 - **C** Volstagg   2 - **B** Egypt   3 - **A** *"Those who would enslave another know only one language ...Brute Force!"*   4 - **B** Gave it to the starving slaves   5 -   6 - **B** A Griffin   7 - Fandrall